# ENVIRONMENTAL AWARENESS

# ENVIRONMENTAL AWARENESS

*A Gower Health and Safety Workbook*

Graham Roberts-Phelps

Gower

© Graham Roberts-Phelps 1999

Published by
Gower Publishing Limited
Gower House
Croft Road
Aldershot
Hampshire GU11 3HR
England

Gower
Old Post Road
Brookfield
Vermont 05036
USA

Graham Roberts-Phelps has asserted his right under the Copyright, Designs and Patents Act 1988 to be identified as the author of this work.

**British Library Cataloguing in Publication Data**
Roberts-Phelps, Graham
    Environmental awareness. – (A Gower health and safety workbook)
    1.Environmental management 2.Conservation of natural resources
    I.Title
    363.7

ISBN 0 566 08063 X

Typeset in Times by Wearset, Boldon, Tyne and Wear and printed in Great Britain by print in black, Midsomer Norton.

# Contents

# Chapter 1
# Introduction

This first chapter acts as a record of your progress through the workbook and provides a place to summarize your notes and ideas on applying or implementing any of the points covered.

# PERSONAL DETAILS

| Name: | |
|---|---|
| Position: | |
| Location: | |
| Date started: | Date completed: |

| Chapter title | Signed | Date |
|---|---|---|
| 1. Introduction | | |
| 2. Understanding the green issues | | |
| 3. Practical measures which you can take | | |
| 4. Reduce, recycle, system, re-use | | |
| 5. Learning review | | |
| 6. Action plan | | |
| Steps taken to implement actions and ideas | | |

| Learning review dates | Assessed by | Date |
|---|---|---|
| 1 month | _____ | _____ |
| 2 months | _____ | _____ |
| 3 months | _____ | _____ |
| 6 months | _____ | _____ |

# HOW TO USE THIS SELF-STUDY WORKBOOK

## Overview

This self-study workbook is designed to be either one, or a combination, of the following:

- ◆ a self-study workbook to be completed during working hours in the student's normal place of work, with a review by a trainer, manager or safety officer at a later date

- ◆ a training programme workbook that can be either fully or partly completed during a training event or events, with the uncompleted sections finished in the student's normal working hours away from the training room.

It contains six self-contained chapters which should each take about 20 minutes to complete, with the final section, 'Learning Review', taking slightly longer due to the testing and validation instruments.

It is essential that students discuss their notes and answers from all sections with a supervisor, trainer or coach.

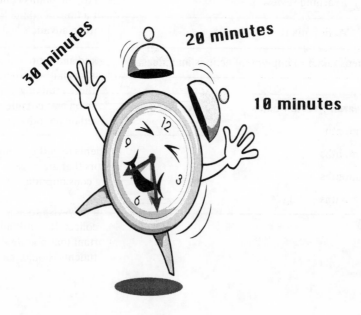

# NOTES FOR TRAINERS AND MANAGERS

## For use in a training session

If you are using the workbook in a training event you might choose to send the manual to students in advance of their attendance, asking them to complete the Introduction (Chapter 1). Other exercises can then be utilized as required during the programme.

## For use as an open-learning or self-study tool

Make sure that you have read the workbook properly yourself and know what the answers are. Anticipate any areas where students may require further support or clarification.

## Comprehension testing

Each section features one or more summary exercises to aid understanding and test retention. The chapter, 'Learning Review', contains a set of tests, case studies and exercises that test application and knowledge. Suggested answers to these are given in the Appendix.

If you are sending the workbook out to trainees, it is advisable to send an accompanying note reproducing, or drawing attention to, the points contained in the section 'Notes for Students'. Also, be sure to set a time deadline for completing the workbook, perhaps setting a review date in advance.

The tests contained in the learning review can be marked and scored as a percentage if required. You might choose to set a 'pass' or 'fail' standard for completion of the workbook, with certification for all those attaining a suitable standard. Trainees who do not reach the required grade on first completion might then be further coached and have points discussed on an individual basis.

Chapter 6, 'Environmental Action Plan', enables students to gather relevant data about consumption of resources, to identify factors that are most important and develop a series of actions for reducing consumption.

Before letting students loose with the Action Plan you may wish to help identify some of the sources of data they will need to collect. It is also advisable to alert them to other people's sensitivities. It is important that no one should feel threatened by their enquiries, which means that students should put some thought into how to gather their data.

# NOTES FOR STUDENTS

This self-study workbook is designed to help you better understand and apply the topic of safe manual handling. It may be used either as part of a training programme, or for self-study at your normal place of work, or as a combination of both.

Here are some guidelines on how to gain the most from this workbook.

- ◆ Find 20 minutes during which you will not be disturbed.

- ◆ Read, complete and review one chapter at a time.

- ◆ Do not rush any chapter or exercise – time taken now will pay dividends later.

- ◆ Complete each written exercise as fully as you can.

- ◆ Make notes of questions or points that come to mind when reading through the sections.

- ◆ Discuss anything that you do not understand with your manager, safety officer or work colleagues.

The final chapter, 'Learning Review', is a scored test that may carry a pass or fail mark.

At regular intervals throughout the workbook there are exercises to complete and opportunities to make notes on any topics or points that you feel are particularly important or relevant to you. These are marked as:

**Notes**

_____

_____

_____

_____

# LEARNING DIARY

**Personal Learning Diary**

Name: _____

Job Title: _____

Company: _____

Date: _____

*The value of the training programme will be greatly enhanced if you complete and review the following Learning Diary before, during and after reviewing and reading the workbook.*

# LEARNING OBJECTIVES

At the start or before completing the workbook, please take time to consider what you would like to learn or be able to do better as a result of the training process. Please be as specific as possible, relating points directly to the requirements of your job or work situation. If possible, please involve your manager, supervisor or team leader in agreeing these objectives.

## Record these objectives below

1.

2.

3.

4.

5.

6.

**PLEASE COMPLETE**
**BEFORE CONTINUING**

# LEARNING LOG

During the training programme there will be many useful ideas and learning points that you will want to apply in the workplace.

| Key ideas/learning points | How I will apply these at work |
|---|---|
|  |  |

**PLEASE COMPLETE**
**BEFORE CONTINUING**

# LEARNING APPLICATION

At the end of each chapter, please consider and identify the specific opportunities for applying the skills, knowledge, behaviours and attitudes and record these below.

| Action planned, with dates | Review/comments |
| --- | --- |
|  |  |

**Remember, it may take time and practice to achieve new results.**
**Review these goals periodically and discuss with your manager.**

**PLEASE COMPLETE**
**BEFORE CONTINUING**

# HOW TO GET THE BEST RESULTS FROM THIS WORKBOOK

The format of this workbook is interactive; it requires you to complete various written exercises. This aids both learning retention and comprehension and, most importantly, acts as a permanent record of completion and learning. It is therefore essential that you **complete all exercises, assignments and questions**.

In order to gain the maximum value and benefit from the time that you invest in completing this workbook, use the following guidelines.

## Pace yourself

You might choose to work through the whole workbook in one session or, alternatively, you might find it easier to take one chapter at a time. This is the recommended approach. If you are using this workbook as part of a live training programme, then make time to follow through any unfinished exercises or topics afterwards.

## Share your own opinions and experience

We all have a different view of the world, and we all have different backgrounds and experiences. As you complete the workbook it is essential that you relate learning points directly to your own situation, beliefs and work environment. Please complete the exercises using relevant examples that are personal and specific to you.

## Keep an open mind

Some of the material you will be covering may be simple common sense, and some of it will be familiar to you. Other ideas may not be so familiar, so it pays to keep an open mind, as most learning involves some form of change. This may take the form of changing your ideas, changing an attitude, changing your perception of what is true, or changing your behaviours and the way you do things.

When we experience change, in almost anything, our first automatic reaction is resistance, but this is not usually the most useful response. Remember, safety is something we have been aware of for a long time, and consider (or fail to consider, as the case may be!) every day. As a result, we follow procedures without thinking – on auto-pilot as it were. This often means that we have a number of bad habits of which we are unaware.

---

*Example of change:*

*Sign your name here as you would normally do:*

*Now hold the pen or pencil in the **opposite** hand to that which you normally use and sign your name again:*

*Apart from noting how difficult this might have been, consider also how 'strange' and uncomfortable this seemed. You could easily learn to sign your name with either hand, usually far more quickly than you might think. However the resistance to change may take longer to overcome.*

---

**Make** *Notes*

Making notes not only gives you information to refer to later, perhaps while reviewing the workbook, but it also aids memory. Many people find that making notes actually helps them to remember things more accurately and for longer. So, as you come across points that are particularly useful or of particular interest, please take a couple of moments to write these down, underline them or make comments in the margin or spaces provided.

**Review with others**

In particular, ask questions and discuss your answers and thoughts with your colleagues and fellow managers, especially points which you are not sure of, points which you are not quite clear on, and perhaps points about which you would like to understand more.

*Before you start any of the main chapters, please complete the following learning assignments.*

# LEARNING OBJECTIVES

It is often said that if you do not know where you are going, any road will get you there. To put it another way, it is difficult to hit the target you cannot see. To gain the most benefit from this workbook, it is best to have some objectives.

## Overall objectives

- ◆ **Improvements.** We don't have to be ill to improve our fitness. Improvement is always possible.

- ◆ **Skills.** Learn new skills, tips and techniques.

- ◆ **Knowledge.** Gain a better understanding of safety issues.

- ◆ **Attitudes.** Change the way we think about safety issues.

- ◆ **Changes.** Change specific attitudes on behaviours and our safety procedures and practice.

- ◆ **Ideas.** Share ideas.

**Here are some areas in which you can apply your overall objectives.**

## 1.　Hazards and risks

The first objective is to be able to identify safety hazards and risks. These may form a part of our surroundings or be things we do as habit.

## 2.　Prevention

Prevention is always better than cure, and part of this workbook will deal with knowing how to prevent environmental damage in the first place. Lack of environmental awareness causes harm in both human and business terms. Damaging the environment affects all of us now and in the future and costs money to put right.

## 3.　Understanding your environmental responsibilities

Looking after the environment is everybody's job, and maintaining environmental awareness is a full-time job. As you complete this workbook you will be looking at how environmental issues affect you personally and the role you can play, not only for your own safety but also the safety of others around you.

## 4. Identifying ways to make the world and your workplace more environmentally friendly

A workbook like this also gives us the opportunity to put ideas together on how we can improve the environment and our workplace. We do not have to have obvious environmental problems in order to improve environmental awareness, any more than we have to be ill to become fitter.

> *Making an improvement to the environment does not have to cost much or be very complicated. Simply recycling paper makes a significant contribution.*

*Make a note here of any personal objectives that you may have.*

**Notes**

_____

_____

_____

_____

_____

# OPINION POLL

Consider the following statements, first marking each with your level of
agreement, and then making some supporting comments regarding these views.

> 5 = **Strongly agree;** 4 = **Agree;** 3 = **Neither agree nor disagree;** 2 = **Disagree;** 1 = **Strongly disagree.**

> 1.  Over the next ten years we must make a dramatic and
>     fundamental shift in our attitudes towards cars,
>     consumption and the environment.

Circle one response: 5  4  3  2  1

Comments:

> 2.  The increasing overuse of road transport has now created
>     less freedom and quality of life, not more.

Circle one response: 5  4  3  2  1

Comments:

> 3.  Consumers, industry and businesses must lead the way in
>     redressing the balance towards a more sustainable and
>     efficient use of the world's resources. Governments around
>     the world are weak in this area.

Circle one response: 5  4  3  2  1

Comments:

> 4.  Being more green, as an organization, is actually cheaper
>     and therefore more profitable.

Circle one response: 5  4  3  2  1

Comments:

> **PLEASE COMPLETE**
> **BEFORE CONTINUING**

## OPINION POLL: REVIEW

> 1. Over the next ten years we must make a dramatic and fundamental shift in our attitudes towards cars, consumption and the environment.

The question is not *if*, but *when* and *how* we change. The signs and beginnings are already there: the reintroduction of trams by town councils; new recycling schemes; and the advent of growing non-politically biased support for environmental and ecological improvements.

> 2. The increasing overuse of road transport has now created less freedom and quality of life, not more.

Cars and road transport cause hundreds of deaths every year. In addition, you probably spend hours every week stuck in stress-inducing traffic jams. The use of this form of transport is out of control. Planners now realize that building new roads is only a short-term solution and that the issue must be tackled at source.

> 3. Consumers, industry and businessess must lead the way in redressing the balance towards a more sustainable and efficient use of the world's resources. Governments around the world are weak in this area.

Governments of the world have a very poor record in these matters. Our best hope is that companies and organizations recognize the market and cost-saving opportunities and act on them.

> 4. Being more green, as an organization, is actually cheaper, and therefore more profitable.

Using less resources and energy saves money.

> **PLEASE COMPLETE**
> **BEFORE CONTINUING**

# Chapter 2
# Understanding the Green Issues

This chapter provides an introduction to the principle causes of environmental pollution, their source and effects, along with some ideas for what we can do about them.

Before starting this chapter, please take a few moments to make a note of any ideas or actions in the learning diary and log in Chapter 1.

# WHAT IS ENVIRONMENTAL AWARENESS?

If there is one thing that marks man out differently from the rest of life on this planet, it is the ability to destroy his natural habitat. This particular skill seems to be unique.

The purpose of this workbook is to explain some of the ways in which we are damaging our own planet, to explain some of these issues and to raise your awareness of their importance.

This workbook looks at the issues, how they affect all of us, what we can do about them – both as individuals and companies – and the importance of this. Several factors underlie the need for greater environmental awareness and action:

- the increasing cumulative effect of pollution and destruction

- the gradual introduction of 'green' legislation

- increasing awareness of customers and consumers

- efficiency savings and opportunities

- the protection of the world for future generations.

# A SHORT HISTORY OF THE UNIVERSE

Think of the planet earth as being a 46 year old person.

The earth is thought to be around 46 million years old, an almost inconceivable time span, particularly in a world where we count the minutes and seconds. This person is a late developer: nothing at all is known about the first seven years and only sketchy information exists about the next 35 years. It is only at the age of 42 that the earth began to support life as we know it.

Dinosaurs and the great reptiles do not appear until a year ago, when this planet was only 45 years old. Mammals arrived only 8 months ago. In the middle of last week human-like apes evolved into ape-like humans, and at the weekend the last ice age enveloped the earth. Modern humans, that is you and me, have been around for about 4 hours. During the last hour we discovered agriculture. The industrial revolution began just 2 minutes ago.

During the last 60 seconds of biological time humans have made a rubbish tip of paradise. We have caused the extinction of many hundreds of species of animals, many of which have been here longer than us, and we have ransacked the planet for fuel. Now we stand, like brutish infants, gloating over this meteoric rise to ascendancy, poised on the brink of the final mass extinction and of effectively destroying this oasis of life in the solar system.[1]

## What is happening?

What are the main environmental challenges, caused by man and affecting our quality of life? They are as follows:

- the greenhouse effect

- air pollution

- ozone depletion

- hazardous waste

- acid rain

- vanishing wildlife

- water conservation

- water pollution

- waste management.

[1] Courtesy of Greenpeace.

# THE GREENHOUSE EFFECT

The 'greenhouse' is a natural effect designed by nature. It allows atmospheric gases to help keep heat in, rather like glass in a greenhouse. However, now, distorted by polluted gases, it is feared – and increasingly being proven – that it may cause a global rise in temperature.

## Example

Motor vehicles release enormous amounts of pollution into the atmosphere every day, and each ingredient in the cocktail of exhaust fumes has a separate effect on our environment.

Annually British cars spew out 4.5 million tonnes of poisonous carbon monoxide, 100 000 tonnes of hydrocarbons (which cause cancer), 2500 tonnes of tetraethyl lead (which can cause brain damage) as well as huge quantities of nitrogen oxides (which react with hydrocarbons to make tree-killing smog) and carbon dioxide (which contributes to the greenhouse effect).

## Greenhouse gases

### Carbon dioxide

- Causes about 50 per cent of the greenhouse effect.

- 20 billion tonnes a year are released.

*Main sources: burning fossil fuels, destruction of rain forests.*

### Chlorofluorocarbons (CFCs)

- Cause about 15–20 per cent of the greenhouse effect and also destroy the ozone layer.

*Main sources: aerosols, industrial processes, heating and cooling elements.*

### Methane

- Causes about 18 per cent of the greenhouse effect.

*Main sources: cattle, rice fields, gas leaks, landfills.*

### Nitrous oxide

- Causes about 10 per cent of the greenhouse effect.

*Main sources: burning fossil fuels, microbes, breakdown of chemical fertilizers.*

### *Ozone*

- ◆ Primary component of smog, normally confined to upper atmosphere.

*Main sources: motor vehicles, power plants, oil refineries.*

# AIR POLLUTION

Pollution from car and lorry exhausts has been increasing alarmingly in recent years. Although little research has been undertaken in the UK to show how this is affecting people's health, evidence from other countries suggests that there is cause for concern.

## The pollutants

The main pollutants from traffic which affect human health are:

◆    carbon monoxide

◆    ozone

◆    nitrogen dioxide

◆    VOCs (volatile organic compounds).

## Road transport accounts for:

◆    90 per cent of carbon monoxide emissions

◆    51 per cent of nitrogen oxides

◆    41 per cent of VOCs.

## Facts and figures

When nitrogen oxides and VOCs combine in sunlight, ozone is produced. Ozone, in this context, refers to low-level ozone – or smog – and should not be confused with the protective ozone layer. Nitrogen dioxide is formed by a chemical reaction involving nitrogen oxides.

◆    Ozone is deadly at ground level.

◆    One in five people are at risk.

◆    Respiratory illness is increasing.

◆    Ozone damages trees and agriculture.

◆    Ozone is caused by cars, trucks, buses, factories, processing plants.

**What can we do?**

◆ Use your car less. Organize your errands so that they can be carried out on a single car journey rather than making multiple trips.

◆ For short journeys either walk or use a bicycle.

◆ Car share for regular trips – for example, to work, school, the supermarket and so on.

◆ Work closer to home.

◆ Drive a car with a high mpg rating.

◆ Have your car serviced regularly.

◆ Travel off-peak to avoid sitting in jams.

◆ Use public transport whenever possible, especially the train, tram or underground.

# OZONE DEPLETION

## Overview

Rectifying ozone depletion is one of the greatest challenges that we face. The problem is immediate and severe, but it is not yet out of control. The ozone layer is still there and we can save it.

Constructive action begins with an understanding of what is causing the depletion, and what each of us can do about it.

The ozone layer is being depleted by man-made gases (chlorofluorocarbons – also called CFCs – and halons) that are found in homes, workplaces and offices worldwide. At one time, CFCs were considered harmless, so manufacturers used them in many different products.

They are still being used today. Freon, used as a coolant in refrigerators, is a CFC. Some types of polystyrene foam, which is often referred to as 'Styrofoam', are still made with CFCs. Contrary to what you might assume, CFCs are not just released in the manufacturing process, they are also released into the atmosphere as the foam breaks or crumbles.

Until very recently, CFCs were commonly used as propellants in aerosol cans. Of the 800 million manufactured in the UK in 1987, 80 per cent contained CFCs. By the end of 1989 over 85 per cent were CFC-free. Yet asthma medication sprays, and video recorder and sewing machine cleaning sprays still use CFCs as propellants. The world's silliest use of CFCs? Canned confetti!

Some fire extinguishers sold for the home and workplace use halons as propellants. Unfortunately, these halons will eventually attack the ozone layer, even if the fire extinguishers are never used, because the ozone-depleting gases gradually leak into the atmosphere.

## What can we do?

- Do not buy halon fire extinguishers.

- Avoid polystyrene foam. This includes form-fitting packing materials – those that protect electronics in boxes, for instance – and foam chips. If you cannot tell whether the foam is made with CFCs, ask. Eventually retailers will pass on your concern to manufacturers.

- If you are planning to use or produce hard foam insulation, make sure that it contains no CFCs. Non-CFC foam insulation is available. It is nearly as effective and will not make a hole in the sky. Consider fibreglass and cellulose insulation too.

◆ Do not buy aerosol cans containing CFCs or, better still, do not use or produce aerosols at all. Even with substitute gases, aerosol sprays are not benign: propane and butane – the hydrocarbons used as propellants in most aerosols today – help create smog when they interact with sunlight. Many products are fitted with non-aerosol ejector pumps. They do not need gases and are just as easy to use.

# HAZARDOUS WASTE

Our modern economy is actually based on consumption. Most products have built-in, almost planned, absolescence. Most of the things that we buy and take home will produce waste packaging and containers. We have been conditioned into developing a 'throw-away' attitude, perhaps largely unaware of the long-term consequences of our actions. The fact is that this 'use, burn or bury' lifestyle is unlikely to be sustainable over the next decade.

For example, do you change your car only because it keeps breaking down or is wearing out? Probably not. Over the last 25–30 years we have all been encouraged to drive new cars and change them regularly. In fact, most modern cars, with regular servicing, would last us 10–20 years, or over 200 000 miles, without any problems.

## Some facts and figures

- In the UK 1 million cars are scrapped each year.

- Every year in the UK 2 billion toilet rolls are used.

- Every year there are 500 million cigarette lighters thrown away in the USA.

- Around 25 pints of tree-killing solvent are emitted into the atmosphere when a single car is painted.

- Britons spend about £30 million per year on garden pesticides.

- Plywood and chipboard emit formaldehyde – one of the home and workplace's biggest indoor pollutants.

- The EU environmental task force has estimated that after 1992 European road freight will increase by 30 per cent. Road freight is the favoured method of transporting hazardous waste.

# ACID RAIN

Pure water has a pH level of 7, which is neutral. 'Acid rain' is the term used for rainfall in which the pH level falls below this figure and is therefore acidic. Its occurrence is attributed to the rise in industrial emissions in the developing world – particularly nitrogen oxide and sulphur dioxide. Whilst it is easy to measure, and experts generally agree on its detrimental effects, the bad news is that solutions are difficult to find and are very unpopular. For example, it would mean all of us changing the way we travel and use our cars, developing new types of car, and rebuilding fossil fuel-burning power stations (a major source of sulphur dioxide) which are now predominant in the emerging industrial nations such as India and China.

## Some facts and figures

- In 1984 black snow, with the same acidic level as vinegar, fell in Aviemore, Scotland.

- Residents of Los Angeles drive 142 million miles – the distance from Earth to Mars – every single day.

- The average car journey in the UK is less than six miles.

- The average car consumes over 2250 gallons of fuel in its lifetime.

- There are an estimated 500 million motor vehicles in use today.

- Every year there are over 400 million batteries sold in the UK.

- Every year 30 million car and lorry tyres are discarded in the UK.

# VANISHING WILDLIFE

As a consequence of our almost total lack of respect and consideration for nature and wildlife in our pursuit of industrial and social development, we are destroying the natural world around us at an alarming rate. This is happening on both a global and local level. For example, parkland, commonland, hedgerows and woodland have all reduced dramatically from one generation to the next and, at the same time, entire species of animals are either being wiped out or threatened with extinction.

## Some facts and figures

- Every year there are 3.5 million medical tests still administered on animals.

- Eighty per cent of all ivory is taken from elephants that are illegally hunted and killed.

- 130 million trees – more than two trees per person – are pulped for paper every year, destroying wildlife habitat.

- The trade in animal furs is still continuing at around 20 million furs per year.

- Every minute an area of tropical rain forest equal to 20 soccer pitches is lost forever.

- In the last three decades 85 per cent of the world's rhinos have been killed for their horns.

## What can we do?

- Buy only products that have not been tested on animals.

- Choose wood and timber from well managed forests.

- Use local nature areas and woodland – use it or lose it!

- Campaign against further erosion of the countryside for development.

- Do not buy products deriving from endangered or rare species – for example, ivory, coral, furs, skins and so on. If there were no market for these products, the animals would be left alone.

# WATER CONSERVATION

Each of us uses around 28 gallons of water every day, while the average British family of four consumes 770 gallons per week. A household can save thousands of gallons of water each year by getting a grip on its taps. Industry uses many times more.

## Some facts and figures

- Every year the average Briton uses 10 000 gallons of water – 500 per cent more than the average Indian.

- A staggering 99.5 per cent of all the fresh water on earth is contained within ice caps and glaciers.

- The biggest domestic water consumer is the toilet – 2.2 gallons for every flush.

- Around 32 per cent of our drinking quality water is flushed down the toilet.

- A running tap probably uses much more water than you think – it puts over two gallons of water down the drain every minute it is on.

- You can easily use between six to 12 gallons of water if you leave the tap running while brushing your teeth.

- Washing dishes with the tap running can use an average of 20 gallons of water.

- If you wash your car at home or at your workplace, using a hose, you can use up to 100 gallons of water.

- It takes half a gallon of water to cook a pot of pasta and a gallon to wash the pot.

- A fraction of 1 per cent of drinkable tap water is actually drunk.

## What can we do?

- Around the workplace and home, be mean with water – it saves money as well as resources for the planet.

- If your industry processes water, rethink, redesign, fit water meters and reduce consumption. Do not use non-biodegradable chemicals or materials.

◆ Arrange for a water meter to be fitted in the home; this will make you more aware of your consumption levels and encourage conservation.

◆ Fit a trigger nozzle to your hose – it will save at least 15 gallons of water every time you wash your car.

◆ Fit a device to the toilet cistern to reduce its capacity or install a dual-flush device allowing a short or long flush.

# WATER POLLUTION

The pollution of the inland waterways, rivers, canals and seas surrounding the United Kingdom is caused by many factors, including:

♦ farm pesticides, seeping from adjoining land, which are usually deadly to all forms of fish

♦ industrial waste and cleaning processes

♦ sewage, which is still pumped untreated into the sea in large quantities – human faeces are still washed up regularly on many of Britain's most popular beaches.

♦ a virus caused by rat urine which is infecting many inland lakes

♦ illegal dumping of chemicals, waste and oil

♦ oil spillage/leaking and the deliberate (and often illegal) dumping of chemicals and waste at sea

♦ washing of oil tanks at sea.

Many experts are of the opinion that the situation is unlikely to improve quickly due to inadequate legislation and the vested interests of powerful companies and groups. For example, little is done to reduce the spiralling rat population as this would involve spending money (profits) and draw attention to the problem. Occasionally, sea or river disasters can catch the headlines for a few days, but little seems to change and the fines imposed on the offending parties are tiny in comparison to the damage that they cause, which may take years to repair. Many more incidents go largely unreported.

## Some facts and figures

♦ Only 3 per cent of the earth's water is fresh water.

♦ Just one part oil per million parts of water will make drinking water smell and taste odd.

♦ One gallon of petrol can contaminate 150 000 gallons of water.

♦ Drinking water generally contains more than 16 toxic pesticides.

♦ Britain is facing an epidemic of rats which live in the sewage systems of most large towns. It is estimated that there are over 40 million rats in the UK.

- Each day 300 million gallons of sewage – most of it untreated or only partially filtered – are pumped into Britain's seas.

## What can we do?

- Encourage the companies we work for to take a responsible, sustainable and sensible approach to using water to clean or disperse waste.

- Wherever possible, choose products and supplies that avoid toxic solvents and use biodegradable chemicals (most leading car manufacturers now do this). If you are a manufacturer, design these factors into your products or goods.

- As consumers, do not pour untreated or toxic chemicals or oil into the drainage system. Use products as described above – for example, water-soluble paints.

- If you are a manager or decision-maker, agree a long-term improvement with your board and shareholders to clean up your act. Also have a contingency plan and budget for the immediate clean-up of any spillages and incidents.

- Choose and use products made of materials that are as natural as possible. Plastics, rubber, polythene and the like all use, and most likely pollute, water in their production.

# WASTE MANAGEMENT

One significant change, started a few years ago, and now being accelerated in all major Western countries, is the proactive reduction and management of waste. Burning our waste causes pollution, as does burying it, and the fact is we are running out of places to bury. Legislation, backed by public opinion, now requires manufacturers and producers to use less waste and make sure that as much of their products and packaging is as biodegradable as possible. For example, car manufacturers will use paint and processes that produce much less waste – particularly toxic waste – and a far higher percentage of their components are recyclable or biodegradable.

## Some facts and figures

◆   About 73 per cent of Britain's paper is thrown away rather than recycled.

◆   Every three months the USA throws away enough aluminium to rebuild its entire commercial airfleet.

◆   In the UK only 14 per cent of glass is recycled, whereas the Netherlands achieves 62 per cent.

◆   If everyone in the UK placed one day's rubbish in Trafalgar Square, the pile would reach up to Nelson's feet.

◆   Soft drinks and beer in Denmark cannot be sold in non-returnable bottles. Such legislation has yet to be considered in the UK.

◆   Of the 13.5 billion cans used annually in the UK, less than 2 per cent are recycled.

◆   By the year 2000 the USA hopes to be recycling 42 per cent of its plastic refuse.

◆   Americans produce enough Styrofoam cups every year to circle the globe 436 times.

◆   About 6 per cent of domestic rubbish is made of plastic.

◆   Britons produce 23 million tons of household refuse every year.

◆   The world's shipping industry dumps over 450 000 plastic containers into the sea every day.

◆   The UK produces around 0.75 million tons of newspaper every year.

- It is calculated, by government officials, that as much as 60 per cent of the UK's household rubbish could be reclaimed.

- The average adult will generate about 600 times their own weight in rubbish in a lifetime.

- We put 1000 tonnes of paper into our dustbins every week.

- A third of British household rubbish is made up of packaging.

- Every year the USA produces the equivalent of 10 lbs of plastic for every person on earth.

- The HM Expectorate of Pollution has found that over 1000 English and Welsh landfills are under threat of explosion caused by methane gas.

## What can we do?

Even for us, as consumers, recycling offers a significant opportunity to really make a difference. Whether this is for glass, clothes, books, batteries, metal, plastic or paper, we must all increase our efforts and also encourage public service bodies to create more facilities for easy recycling opportunities.

# HOW GREEN IS YOUR ORGANIZATION?

The main objective of this exercise is to introduce the subject of environmental awareness in a general sense and discover your attitudes, experience and perception of your organization's record of environmental awareness, particularly in relation to others and perhaps in relation to how it could be improved.

*Do you think your organization is particularly 'green' in comparison with other organizations, or could it be doing more in this respect? (Give examples and reasons.)*

> **PLEASE COMPLETE**
> **BEFORE CONTINUING**

# Chapter 3
# Practical
# Measures Which
# You Can Take

Now that you have become aware of the principal causes of environmental pollution, this chapter shows you how you can improve your personal and work practices.

Before starting this chapter, please take a few moments to make a note of any ideas or actions in the learning diary and log in Chapter 1.

# SIMPLE THINGS TO SAVE THE PLANET

There is nothing very complicated about being 'green'. Indeed, many of the ideas are basic common sense, but unfortunately not common practice. We have created organizations, businesses, homes, workplaces and lifestyles that are directly at odds with a sustainable existence and an assured future for our children. The persistent campaigning of groups such as Friends of the Earth and Greenpeace have led to environmental issues being taken increasingly more seriously by governments worldwide. Consequently, we are beginning to see the first stages of 'Polluter Pays' legislation being introduced in Europe. Under this legislation the companies and organizations which produce the pollution will have to pay in order to compensate society for cleaning it up and for the loss of quality of life due to it.

*What can we do?*
*'Nobody made a greater mistake than*
*he who did nothing because he could only*
*do little.'*

For example, none of us really pays the true cost of motoring or road transport. If we paid an amount that reflects the cost of motoring and pollution to the environment it would cost us many more times than it does now. In this workbook we will look at the six ways in which we can all take a big step forward not only creating a sustainable personal future, but also a sustainable economic future for our businesses and organizations.

We should not make the mistake of thinking that because we can only do a little, we should do nothing at all. No matter how small or insignificant it may seem in isolation, every action we take makes a difference.

*Make a note of any actions you could take that would contribute in some way to environmental conservation.*

**Notes**

_____

_____

_____

# PRACTICAL GREEN AWARENESS AT WORK

## Overview

Most of the environmental conservation measures that you can take at home apply in the workplace too. It is not always easy to implement them, but it is worth it. A huge volume of the earth's resources is consumed at business level and an enormous amount can be saved. You may even be rewarded with that long-awaited pay rise, by proposing some sort of recycling scheme which saves your company a fortune.

## Some facts and figures

- Each tonne of recycled paper saves more than three cubic yards of landfill space.

- Every tonne of recycled office paper saves about 350 gallons of oil.

- Every year Americans throw away enough office and writing paper to build a wall 12 feet high, stretching from New York to Los Angeles.

## What can we do as individuals?

It is easy to make a small individual contribution. Here are some examples:

- Bring a coffee cup to work rather than use disposable cups.

- Re-use manila envelopes by putting sticky labels over the old addresses. Any stationer should have them.

You can also work on more ambitious projects with your colleagues:

- Set up glass and aluminium can recycling programmes. This usually entails putting containers for saving bottles and cans in a prominent place and organizing a rota to decide who takes them to the recycling centre when they are full.

- Set up a special environmental bulletin board and post notices with interesting titbits and statistics about conservation. Include photographs where appropriate.

- Substitute paper cups, which are biodegradable, for styrofoam cups, which are not.

- Set up a paper recycling programme. There is a simple procedure. Each employee saves paper at their desk, sorting paper into recyclable groups, as it is discarded, into desktop containers. Then introduce a collection system. Friends of the Earth have started to sponsor such schemes in many offices.

- Try to obtain a two-sided Xerox machine. Or, if you have one already, make sure that everyone makes double-sided copies wherever possible. This will save thousands of pages when copying lengthy reports.

- Carry out an energy audit to assess your office's use of electricity and other resources. It can make a huge difference. Areas for making savings will be readily identifiable and will make a huge difference not only in terms of conservation but also to the company's costs.

- If some of your firm's company cars or other vehicles run on leaded petrol, lobby your supervisor to replace them.

*Make a note on anything from this section that you need to act on.*

**Notes**

_____

_____

_____

_____

_____

_____

_____

# GREEN SENSE IS BUSINESS SENSE

It may come as a surprise to many business people that being 'green' also means being more profitable. The basic premise of a sustainable economy is that of a frugal, efficient and profitable organization.

Notwithstanding 'Polluter Pays' legislation, or more expensive taxes on motoring and other forms of pollution, becoming more aware of the principles of environmental awareness can actually improve business performance, whether this is in terms of reduced costs or in attracting new customers and creating new markets.

**Consider:**

- using less power (saves money, increases profits)

- using less fuel (saves money, increases profits)

- using less paper (saves money, increases profits)

- using less chemicals (saves money, increases profits)

- using less packing (saves money, increases profits)

- using less processing (saves money, increases profits)

- using less distribution (saves money, increases profits)

- commuting less (improves productivity, increases profits)

- creating less waste and pollution (improves productivity, increases profits and can also save money).

*Make a note of any ways in which your office or workplace can become more 'green'.*

**Notes**

_____

_____

_____

_____

_____

_____

_____

_____

# CARS AND MOTOR VEHICLES

## Drive less!

### Overview

Using cars and the use of road transport for distribution is probably the single most damaging contribution we make to the environment. We must all attempt to cut down on the amount of driving we do.

### Facts and figures

- In 1987, 29 per cent of the UK's energy resources was consumed by transport.

- By 1985, 90 per cent of passenger miles in the UK were travelled by road.

- A bike uses up little space, releases no pollution and provides healthy exercise.

- The car uses up 50 times more energy in its production than it will in its lifetime.

- If only 1 per cent of the car owners in the USA left their cars idle for one day per week, it would save an estimated 35 million gallons of petrol per year. This would reduce destructive emissions accordingly – around 840 million pounds of carbon dioxide would be kept out of the atmosphere.

- Motorways make up only 15 per cent of the UK road network yet carry 60 per cent of the traffic.

### What can we do?

The average number of miles travelled to and from work by car commuters is only 37 miles per week. This means that the typical car journey to work is less than four miles. If you make regular short journeys by car, consider the alternatives. Try using another means of transport – such as buses, trains, bicycles, the underground or walking – just one day per week. It may be difficult, but it is worth the effort.

Other societies have managed to cut down on their use of cars.

- In the Netherlands 80 per cent of train commuters travel to the station by bicycle.

- In Denmark about 30 per cent of all trips are taken by bicycle.

- Japan has bicycle parking garages in urban areas.

## Catalytic converters

### Overview

Motor vehicles release enormous amounts of pollution into the atmosphere every day, and each ingredient in the cocktail of exhaust fumes has a separate effect on our environment.

### Facts and figures

Annually British cars spew out 4.5 million tonnes of poisonous carbon monoxide, 100 000 tonnes of hydrocarbons (which cause cancer), 2500 tonnes of tetraethyl lead (which can cause brain damage) as well as huge quantities of nitrogen oxides (which react with hydrocarbons to make tree-killing smog) and carbon dioxide (which contributes to the greenhouse effect).

### What can we do?

A catalytic converter, which cleans up the gases that cars emit, can be built into the exhaust system.

## Car-sharing

### Overview

The growing number of cars on the roads poses an enormous threat to the environment, yet, for many, there are few alternatives.

### Facts and figures

- It has been estimated that, by the year 2000, the UK will have constructed another 900 miles of major roads and motorways, damaging Sites of Special Scientific Interest (SSSIs) and robbing the UK of valuable countryside.

- Each mile of a six-lane motorway consumes 25 acres of land.

- 54 per cent of journeys made to work in the UK are made by car.

- 65 per cent of people who need to travel for their work do so by car.

### What can we do?

Although car-sharing has never been seriously considered in this country, some environmentalists believe that it may yet prove an effective way of cutting down on car journeys and their harmful byproducts.

Try setting up a car-sharing programme in your area. If you make regular journeys – to work, for instance, or to visit a relative on the same day every week – place a notice in your local post office or newspaper. It is likely that at least one other person is making the same trip in another car and will be willing to share the journey.

Try a shared car ownership scheme in which a number of families buy a car jointly and use it mainly for large loads or difficult journeys. All participants buy public transport passes too and each has a key to the car. Mileage is logged and paid to the treasurer. One consequence may be that, as people discover alternative means of travel or learn to cut down on unnecessary journeys, the car is used less and less.

## At the petrol station

### Overview

The type of petrol we choose has an impact on the environment.

### Facts and figures

Leaded petrol is an environmental hazard. Airborne lead from vehicle exhaust causes liver, kidney and brain damage in humans. Scientists suspect that it is responsible for damaging crops as well. Motor vehicles in Britain are responsible for the release of over 2500 tonnes of lead into the air.

### What can we do?

If you do not have a fairly new car or have not already changed to unleaded petrol, find out whether your car can take it. Some older cars can run on either leaded or unleaded.

Butane, a component of petrol, helps create ozone smog when it evaporates. So when you fill your petrol tank, the escaping vapours pollute the atmosphere. In the USA plastic hoods have been introduced on many petrol pump nozzles to control these vapours. The special hood fits over the tank opening and sucks fumes into the underground storage tank, preventing the vapours from escaping. More and more US states are requiring petrol stations to install such equipment. Ask your regular petrol station what their company is doing to prevent the escape of butane, or write to your MP to express your concern.

## Drive efficiently

### Overview

We all know that cars have a serious impact on the environment, but, because we depend on them in our everyday lives, it is unrealistic to suggest that people stop driving altogether.

Even if you drive every day, there is something simple that you can do to help the environment: make sure that your car is running as efficiently as possible. Getting good mileage out of your petrol is not just a matter of economics – a fuel-efficient vehicle is less destructive to our planet than a petrol hog.

### Facts and figures

- Worldwide, there are an estimated 500 million motor vehicles in use today of which about 350 million are cars. In the UK alone there are around 23 million petrol-driven vehicles.

- Annually, UK road transport emits about 105 million tonnes – 18 per cent of total emissions – of carbon dioxide $CO_2$, the key ingredient in the greenhouse effect. The volume of $CO_2$ emitted by a car is directly related to the amount of petrol it uses.

- Road vehicles also cause acid rain by emitting nitrogen oxides. In recent years motor vehicle emissions of nitrogen dioxide have risen to over 1000 million tonnes per year, around 45 per cent of total emissions. This figure would be reduced by burning less petrol.

- Annually, Europe releases out 550 000 tonnes of hydrocarbons into the air, of which about a quarter comes from road vehicles. These cause tree-killing and lung-damaging ozone smog. Again, this effect is directly related to the amount of fuel consumed.

- Around 4.5 million tonnes of poisonous carbon monoxide are released in the UK every year – about 83 per cent deriving from motor vehicles. This, too, can be reduced by cutting down on petrol usage.

**All these figures are increasing rapidly!**

### What can we do?

- Keep your car and commercial vehicles tuned and running efficiently. This is the easiest way to make your car more fuel-efficient. A well tuned car, van or lorry uses up to 9 per cent less petrol than a poorly tuned one. That means a 9 per cent reduction in toxic emissions. Bear in mind, also, that owners of vehicles emitting excessive fumes can be fined and even have their vehicles banned from the road.

- Keep track of your petrol consumption. If there is a sudden drop in your mileage per gallon, have the problem identified and remedied.

- Do not let your engine idle unnecessarily as this uses more petrol than restarting the engine. Idling becomes less energy-efficient than restarting your car or engine after about a minute.

- Drive sensibly. Excessive acceleration and sudden braking increase fuel consumption.

- Keep fuel filters clean. Clogged filters use more petrol.

- Stay light. Check to see whether you are hauling around unnecessary weight in your car. Surprisingly, an extra 100 lbs will decrease your fuel economy by more than 1 per cent.

- Little things help. For example, if 100 000 car owners who have previously neglected to do so, started to have their cars tuned regularly, some 90 million pounds of carbon dioxide could be kept out of the atmosphere every year.

**If you are buying a new vehicle:**

- Check the fuel economy figures and compare specifications.

- Keep fuel efficiency in mind. Remember, a car which achieves an average of 26.5 mpg will emit 20 tonnes less carbon monoxide in its lifetime than the average car on the road today. You can now buy cars which will achieve 55 mpg, and some prototypes can get up to 100 mpg.

- Weigh options carefully. Optional equipment, such as power steering and automatic transmissions, require a great deal of energy. Other extras, such as electrically operated windows or power brakes, do not use as much, but still add to a car's weight and reduce fuel economy.

*Make a note on how you could implement some of the ideas from this section.*

**Notes**

---

---

---

---

---

---

---

---

# RAISING ENVIRONMENTAL AWARENESS

The purpose of this exercise is to examine one very important issue regarding environmental awareness – encouraging and enforcing a wiser, more sustainable approach.

Every day, intelligent and informed people ignore basic common-sense environmental working and contribute to the world's environmental problems. Have you ever considered why this is?

Complete the following exercise in detail.

1.  *Consider carefully some of the actions that you and others could take, on a day-to-day basis, to reduce the damage to the environment and increase our enjoyment of it.*

2.  *Consider practical ways to encourage people to take environmental issues more seriously.*

PLEASE COMPLETE
BEFORE CONTINUING

# SELF-ASSESSMENT WORKSHEET

Please complete the following questionnaire, as honestly and accurately as you can. Rate your response to each statement or question on the following scale:

**1 = Never; 2 = Sometimes; 3 = Usually; 4 = Often; 5 = Always.**

| | |
|---|---|
| 1. I always recycle newspapers and waste paper, using local recycling facilities | 1 2 3 4 5 |
| 2. I always recycle bottles, plastics and tins | 1 2 3 4 5 |
| 3. I use two sides of paper when writing reports or memos | 1 2 3 4 5 |
| 4. I use the reverse side of paper for scrap and notepaper | 1 2 3 4 5 |
| 5. I am careful when selecting suppliers to check whether the content of products are as environmentally sound as possible | 1 2 3 4 5 |
| 6. Whenever practical, I use the telephone instead of sending a letter or memo | 1 2 3 4 5 |
| 7. Where possible, I choose products which have the least packaging | 1 2 3 4 5 |
| 8. I drive in a fuel-economic manner that uses less fuel | 1 2 3 4 5 |
| 9. I use public transport whenever I can | 1 2 3 4 5 |
| 10. I often walk or cycle for short journeys | 1 2 3 4 5 |
| 11. I input environmental issues into planning and discussions | 1 2 3 4 5 |
| 12. I take steps to reduce mileage travelled on business | 1 2 3 4 5 |
| 13. Whenever possible, I source products and supplies from local suppliers to avoid unnecessary distribution costs | 1 2 3 4 5 |
| 14. Waste products produced by the organization are treated and disposed of properly | 1 2 3 4 5 |
| 15. Whenever possible, I repair equipment rather than replace it in order to avoid unnecessary extra consumption | 1 2 3 4 5 |

**cont'd**

| | |
|---|---|
| 16. I avoid, when possible, the use of CFCs and products containing dangerous chemicals or which involve damaging production processes | 1 2 3 4 5 |
| 17. I switch off machines, equipment and lights that are not being used | 1 2 3 4 5 |
| 18. I use rechargeable batteries rather than the disposable type | 1 2 3 4 5 |
| 19. I encourage those around me to think in a more environmentally friendly fashion | 1 2 3 4 5 |
| 20. I select low-energy-consumption equipment, such as long-life light bulbs and so on | 1 2 3 4 5 |

My score is _____/100      or _____%

## Analysis

Between 80%–100%      Excellent.
Between 60%–80%        Very good.
Between 40%–60%        OK.
Less than 40%          Room for improvement!

*How could you improve on your score from this assessment?*

**Notes**

_____

_____

_____

_____

_____

| |
|---|
| **PLEASE COMPLETE BEFORE CONTINUING** |

# Chapter 4
# Reduce, Recycle,
# Renew, Re-use

This chapter concentrates on ways of reducing consumption, recycling or re-using some of the most common resources at home and in the workplace.

Before starting this chapter, please take a few moments to make a note of any ideas or actions in the learning diary and log in Chapter 1.

# WAYS TO REDUCE CONSUMPTION

One of the simplest and yet most effective things we can do to help our environment, as well as the cost base of our company, is actually to reduce the amount of energy and resources that we use on a daily basis. Over the last few years many companies have introduced cost-cutting schemes, mainly driven by economic conditions.

Many have been surprised at the benefit which these programmes have brought and how little impact they have on the organization's functioning productivity. For instance, many large buildings now feature energy management systems which turn lights on and off automatically, depending on whether or not people are in the room. Some buildings have advanced heating systems which recycle heat to other parts of the building.

On an individual basis, there are hundreds of everyday ways in which we can reduce our energy and resource consumption.

*REDUCE . . .*
*Paper*
*Electric, heat, light, power*
*Business miles*
*Distribution*
*Packaging*

Take a moment to list as many ways as you can think of. For example, simply turning the lights off when they are not needed can save hundreds of pounds worth of electricity over the course of a year. If every business in the UK did this, it would both reduce pollution by millions of tons and the need for less power stations.

### Reducing heating

#### Overview

The most important way in which people can save energy in their home or workplace is to make sure that their boilers are running efficiently. More domestic energy is used for heating than for any other purpose.

#### Facts and figures

- ◆ Nearly 70 per cent of the energy that we use in the home or workplace is used to heat rooms.

- The average home and workplace in the UK costs between £300 and £400 per year to keep warm.

- Over 100 000 tonnes of sulphur dioxide are released annually from British households.

- About 27 per cent of British carbon dioxide emissions come from domestic space heating.

### What can we do?

Your heating bill can be reduced by about 8 per cent for every degree by which you turn your temperature thermostat down.

Advisers suggest that boilers are serviced once a year. This could cut down your energy use by 5 per cent. British Gas runs schemes for the aftercare and servicing of heating boilers.

Make some reflectors by taping aluminium foil to pieces of cardboard and placing them behind your radiators. This saves energy and money by throwing back heat which you would normally have lost through the walls.

### Reducing lighting

### Overview

The simple action of turning a light switch on and off affects the environment. The more electricity we use, the more emissions we generate from power stations, contributing heavily to such problems as the greenhouse effect and acid rain.

There are several simple ways to 'light right'. The most obvious is conservation – diligently turning lights off when they are not in use. But a less obvious and more effective method is to choose and use your light bulbs with energy conservation in mind.

### Facts and figures

- An ordinary 100W light bulb has a lifespan of about 1000 hours. During that time it will consume about £7 worth of electricity.

- Most people are unaware of the development of the compact fluorescent light bulb. This amazing bulb screws into the standard sockets and gives off light that looks just like a traditional light bulb – nothing like the fluorescent light we are used to seeing in factories, schools and offices. These bulbs are big energy-savers. They last ten times longer, and use about 75 per cent less electricity, than an ordinary bulb.

- Substituting a compact fluorescent light bulb for a traditional bulb will keep half a tonne of carbon dioxide out of the atmosphere over the bulb's lifetime.

- Compact fluorescent lights are more expensive to buy than traditional bulbs, but studies have shown that the real cost of an ordinary bulb is the initial price, plus five to 10 times the costs in electricity. So the cost of a compact fluorescent will generally save money as well as the environment.

- Compact fluorescent lights are not suitable for every type of lighting situation. One factor is size – they will not work in small lamps and certain covered fixtures. Another factor is frequency of use; they are best used in places where they are left on for at least two hours per day. Also, the life of a compact fluorescent bulb can be reduced at low temperatures, so enclose the bulb in a glass fitting if you are using it outside.

- If a single compact fluorescent bulb was installed in each of 1 million houses, the energy equivalent of about 600 000 traditional bulbs would be saved.

### What can we do?

Interestingly, one high-wattage ordinary bulb is more efficient than two small ones in a multi-bulb fixture. For example, a 100W bulb generates about as much light as two 60W bulbs, and it saves energy. In light fixtures that take three bulbs, try using only two. But for safety's sake put a burned-out bulb in the last socket.

In addition try more efficient bulbs such as long-life, krypton-filled, tungsten halogen and infrared-reflective coated.

### Junk mail

### Overview

We do not usually think of junk mail as an environmental problem, just a nuisance. But the unwanted paper we receive through our letter boxes every year accounts for millions of wasted trees.

### Facts and figures

- Because of the way it is distributed, no one really knows how much true junk mail – that is, mail that is addressed to 'The Occupier' or that which is not addressed at all – is received.

- Professionally targeted direct mail is now big business in the UK, Europe and the USA. Just consider how many direct mail letters, brochures and catalogues you receive in an average week. Why not count them – for both work and home? The total might be anything from 30 to 300!

- ◆ Junk mail is encouraged by making incentives and policies that enable bulk mailers to send material at reduced rates.

### What can we do?

Make sure that you only request brochures that you are really interested in or need. Most responsible companies offer you a choice **not** to receive future mail and **not** to have your name and address sold on to other companies, so be sure to select this option. Return any unsolicited and unrequested mail unopened, first writing on the envelope (or affix a label printed off from your PC) 'UNWANTED MAIL. PLEASE REMOVE MY NAME AND ADDRESS FROM YOUR DATABASE IMMEDIATELY'.

Recycle the junk mail you already receive. If it is printed on newsprint, throw it in with the newspapers. If it is quality paper, recycle it separately. Self-seal envelopes and those with plastic windows cannot be recycled. Gummed evelopes are fine.

*This is what we can save!*

### Detergents

### Overview

Phosphates – chemical compounds containing phosphorus – are found in most detergents, washing powders and liquids. They soften water and prevent dirt particles from being redeposited on clothes.

Unfortunately their use has several ecological side-effects. As phosphates empty into rivers and lakes they cause algae bloom – that is, they fertilize algae to the point where it grows out of control. When, in its natural cycle, algae dies, the bacteria that cause it to decay require huge amounts of oxygen which is needed by other plants and marine life to survive. Result: lakes and streams can die.

## Facts and figures

- Up to 30 per cent of most detergents or washing powders are made up of phosphates.

- More than 25 per cent of the phosphate in our fresh water is derived from the detergents.

- Other components of detergents include enzymes, which can cause allergic skin reactions, and bleaches, fluorescers and perfumes – none of which are quick to biodegrade.

## What can we do?

- Use a little less detergent. Manufacturers tend to recommend more detergent than necessary.

- Use a phosphate-free detergent. Such products, which are now widely available, are designed to biodegrade within five days.

- If your detergent claims to be 'biological', it means that it contains enzymes. You should avoid enzymes if you have sensitive skin.

*Make a note on how you could implement some of the ideas from this section.*

**Notes**

_____

_____

_____

_____

# WAYS TO RE-USE

Once we have reduced our use of energy and resources, we can then turn our attention to see how much we might be able to re-use. A walk around any office, warehouse or factory will find dozens of examples of items that can be re-used, instead of buying new.

For instance, many organizations are now adopting policies of using both sides of sheets of paper. Paper which has been used on one side only can be re-used for fax machines, draft copies, notepads or draft printing. Likewise, boxes, plastic packing and even envelopes can be re-used, either internally or externally, or for suppliers and so on. I am sure that your supplier would not mind receiving their next invoice payment in a re-used envelope. They would probably be so pleased with the payment they wouldn't even notice!

*RE-USE . . .*
*Paper*
*Packaging and containers*
*Envelopes*

Many companies think that the customers might object to such a policy but they might actually be impressed. Take a moment now to make a list of everything in your work area that you could begin to re-use. Do not worry how small or insignificant it may seem; the overall effect can be quite far-reaching.

## Re-use old paper

### Overview

In the UK we only recycle a few million tonnes of waste paper per year – about 25–30 per cent of the total. If we were to increase this, even by a relatively small percentage, millions of trees would be left standing every year.

### Facts and figures

- It takes 15 trees to make 1 tonne of virgin paper.

- Over 8.7 million tonnes of paper are consumed annually in the UK.

- Making new paper from old paper uses only 10 per cent of the water and 50 per cent of the energy used in making paper from trees, and it reduces related air pollution by over 75 per cent.

- Recycled paper could easily be substituted for virgin paper in many products without any loss in quality but, because the demand for it has been low, the price of recycled paper tends to be higher than that of virgin stock. This, in turn, makes recycled paper more difficult to obtain. Result: manufacturers which could use recycled paper do not bother.

♦ The markets for high-grade waste paper are reliable and tend not to fluctuate. Waste paper merchants grade paper according to type, from computer listing paper (top grade) to newspaper, magazines and cardboard. Again, because current demand is limited, some waste paper collected may still have to be dumped. If we bought more paper recycled from the lower grades, then waste paper merchants could sell off their glut.

♦ Recycled paper is usually cheaper than virgin equivalents in both the Netherlands and Germany. The UK recycles only 35 per cent of its paper; in the Netherlands the figure is 50 per cent.

## What can we do?

Newspapers, magazines and computer reports are probably the easiest material to recycle, since they lie around the house or office anyway. Recycling them is a simple way to get into the recycling habit. But remember that other types of paper and card are recyclable, too.

1. **Save them.** Do not throw newspapers or computer reports out with the rubbish. Sort them. Magazines, with their coloured paper and coated covers, are not easily recyclable. Stack them and donate them to doctor's surgeries, hospitals and other institutions for re-use. The key to a personal recycling programme is to have a specific place in your home and workplace for discarded paper.

2. **Recycle them.** Look in the *Yellow Pages* to find your local paper merchant. Ask which types of paper are most in demand, and whether a container loan for one morning per month is possible.

   Otherwise, drop paper off in the designated receptacles at supermarkets, shopping centres, recycling centres and the like. Contact your local authority, recycling plant or an environmental group, such as Friends of the Earth, for more help and information.

3. **Buy it!** Create a demand for recycled paper by requesting it at your stationers and suppliers.

## Recharge your batteries

### Overview

Batteries which are thrown out with the garbage are taken to landfill sites where they corrode and break apart, releasing dangerous mercury or cadmium into the soil. Batteries that are incinerated with garbage release mercury or cadmium into the air.

## *Facts and figures*

♦ Every year around 400 million batteries are sold in the UK.

♦ Prolonged exposure to mercury can not only make people seriously ill but can even affect behaviour. In the 1600s hat makers who used mercury to treat felt and fur began to act strangely. Since no one knew that the hatters were showing the effects of mercury poisoning, it was assumed that they were just crazy. Hence the expression 'mad as a hatter', and the Mad Hatter in *Alice in Wonderland*.

♦ In France batteries account for over 80 per cent of domestic mercury emissions. The production of mercury oxide batteries is prohibited in Denmark. Legislation in other countries is gradually appearing.

♦ Around 30 per cent of the cadmium used worldwide goes into batteries.

## *What can we do?*

♦ Use mercury-free or cadmium-free batteries for preference.

♦ Use rechargeable batteries. Although they do contain cadmium, they last 500 times longer than alkaline batteries, and thus contribute a little less to our hazardous waste problem.

♦ Use mains power instead of batteries wherever possible.

*Make a note of any items in your home and workplace that could be re-used.*

**Notes**

_____

_____

_____

_____

# WAYS TO RECYCLE

Recycling is the process that springs to most people's minds when they think of environmental awareness or becoming 'green'. Recycling stations are now commonplace in our high streets and outside our superstores, and many of us are beginning to use them. However, the percentage of recyclable products that we actually recycle is still very small, and one of the reasons for this is because business is a large user of paper, packing and other materials and doesn't recycle as general policy.

Many companies are now adopting programmes of recycling, and setting up collection points in corridors, workplaces and canteens. If your company does not have such a recycling scheme, then maybe you could consider starting one. Alternatively if you already have one, maybe you could look at ways to increase its coverage or encourage people to use it. There may also be items which you are not recycling that can be, and there are many new items that are becoming recyclable as new technology becomes available. For instance, aluminium, glass, tin, metal, different types of paper, plastic, cardboard, scrap metal, timber, batteries and many other items now have a market as recyclable items.

Make a list of some of the things which you could recycle more effectively within your organization, or list items which you would like to start recycling.

## Starting a recycling programme in your home, office or workplace

### Overview

By now, you should be excited about recycling. But what do you do if you discover that there is no recycling programme in your area?

### Setting up

- If you are thinking about starting a plastic recycling programme in your area, contact the British Plastics Federation, 5 Belgrave Square, London SW1X 8PH. They will be delighted to help.

- You could earn money by organizing a local aluminium collection scheme. For information write to Alcan Enfield Alloys Ltd, Barnet Road, London Colney, St Albans, Hertfordshire AL2 1DN.

- Advice on voluntary collections of most items can be obtained from the National Anti-Waste Programme, Ashdown House, 123 Victoria Street, London SW1 6RB.

- Contact your local branch of Friends of the Earth for advice and information.

- Search the Internet to find out more about local schemes.

- Local councils throughout the UK are stepping up their environmental programmes and should be a good source of help and advice.

## Recycling glass

### *Overview*

People have been making glass for approximately 3500 years. Most glass is made of three basic ingredients: white sand, soda and lime.

The materials are heated to around 1200°C, until they are completely dissolved and transparent. Then the mixture is cooled to around 900°C. It takes about 7600 BTUs of energy to produce a single pound of glass.

Before recycled glass is shipped to the manufacturers, it is broken so that it takes up less space. This broken glass is called cullet. When it arrives at the factory, the cullet is run through a magnetic device designed to remove rings from bottles. A vacuum process removes plastic coatings and paper labels, then the cullet is ready to be added to the mixture.

Because cullet lowers the melting temperature of the glass manufacturing mixture, up to 32 per cent less energy is required. This is a huge saving when you consider how much glass we produce every year.

### *Facts and figures*

- Annually, in the UK, we use about 6 billion bottles and jars, which is the equivalent of over 1.5 million tonnes of glass.

- The energy saved from recycling one glass bottle will light a 100W bulb for four hours.

- All glass bottles and jars can be recycled. But other types of glass, such as window panes, Pyrex and light bulbs are made by different processes and cannot be combined with the cullet from which glass containers are made.

- Every tonne of recycled glass saves 30 gallons of oil which would be required if it were processed from raw materials.

- Most, if not all, local authorities, and many large shops, now have bottle banks, through which some 16 per cent of our glass containers are recycled.

- In Europe about 31 per cent of glass is recycled; the Netherlands recycles 62 per cent. The UK lies second from bottom in the league table of European glass recycling.

- Glass produced from recycled glass instead of raw material reduces related air pollution by 20 per cent and water pollution by 50 per cent.

- Because glass takes so long to decompose, the bottle you throw away today may still be littering the landscape in the year 3000.

### What can we do?

The easiest way to recycle glass at home and workplace is to organize your garbage so that you can separate and save bottles in a convenient way, either indoors or outdoors. For example, keep a box for glass in a cupboard, or buy a plastic rubbish bin to keep outside. Store the glass as you discard it.

Sort the bottles according to colour: clear, green and brown. Remove any corks or metal caps which cannot be removed magnetically. Do not worry about paper labels. Rinsing is sometimes suggested, but is not absolutely necessary – ask your local recycling centre.

Once you have a place to store the bottles it only take about 15 minutes per week to maintain the process and periodically deliver the glass to your bottle bank.

Not enough glass is being recycled in this country. Encourage your local authority to increase the amount of bottle banks in your area. In addition, lobby your supermarket to promote the return of bottles for recycling. One way would be to promote the use of returnable bottles that require deposits.

### Recycling metal tins and cans

### Overview

Aluminium is the world's most abundant metal, but it was only discovered in the 1820s. At that time it was worth more than gold. The first aluminium drink can appeared in 1963, and these cans now account for the largest single use of aluminium.

### Facts and figures

- The UK has to import aluminium because it does not have economically viable deposits of aluminium ore. It is therefore vital that we recycle.

- When you throw out one aluminium can you waste as much energy as you would do if you fill the same can half-full of petrol and pour it down the drain.

- The UK uses over 13 billion cans per year – about half of which are aluminium and half tin-plated steel. Less than 2 per cent are recycled.

- Every year we throw away about 2.5 million tonnes of metal, valued at more than £1 billion.

- The production of aluminium is highly energy-intensive – manufacturing one tonne requires four tonnes of bauxite.

- Recycling aluminium cuts related air pollution by 95 per cent.

- Manufacturing recycled aluminium uses 95 per cent less energy than making aluminium from scratch.

- If you throw an aluminium can out of your car window, it will still be littering the earth up to 500 years later.

- If you throw away two aluminium cans, you waste more energy than is used daily by each of a billion human beings in the developing world.

- The energy saved from one recycled aluminium can will operate a television set for three hours.

### *What can we do?*

The simplest way of extracting steel cans from household rubbish is by using a magnet. At present, only a few local authorities use magnets to reclaim steel cans. If more councils extracted steel in this way, then virtually every steel can could be recycled. We must lobby councils to introduce steel can recycling schemes.

Aluminium recycling is a profitable business, worth over £500 per tonne. However, the recycling of aluminium is yet to really take off in the UK – there are so far only a few hundred local authority aluminium can banks. Telephone your local council to find out the location of can recycling banks in your area.

If there are facilities for recycling steel scrap or cans in your area, then separate them out. Remove food, rinse the cans and then crush them to save space.

Remember also that other aluminium items can be recycled: these include kitchen foil, ring pulls, cigarette foil (extract the paper), foil baking containers and the foil from milk bottle tops and yoghurt tops. Contact your local council for information.

*Make a note on how you could implement some of the ideas
from this section.*

**Notes**

_____

_____

_____

_____

_____

_____

_____

# WHAT TO REFUSE

Once you have begun to reduce your consumption, re-use items that are re-usable, channel waste into recycling, the next step is to start to refuse excessive packaging and wastage that exists all around us. For example, when you are shopping, if you don't really need to take another plastic bag, you should refuse to do so. If you have a cupboard full of them perhaps you could re-use those. If you are dealing with suppliers, ask them not to overdo the packaging and to be considerate and careful with their use of resources. They may actually be able to save you some money as well as themselves. Take a moment to consider instances where you could refuse the level of packaging or material.

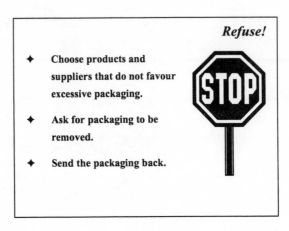

*Refuse!*

✦ **Choose products and suppliers that do not favour excessive packaging.**

✦ **Ask for packaging to be removed.**

✦ **Send the packaging back.**

## Hidden toxins

### *Overview*

Just because you bought something in a shop does not mean that it is safe. There are a surprising number of toxins in your home and workplace, hidden in everything from oven and drain cleaners to personal care products.

They are a hazard, not only to you and your colleagues and family when they are used, but also to the environment both when they are first manufactured and when they are finally disposed of.

What makes these products particularly insidious is the fact that millions of pounds are spent every year in convincing us that they are necessary and will enhance our lives, when in fact they are dangerous.

Happily there are many inexpensive, easy to use, natural alternatives which you can substitute for common commercial chemical products. It just takes a little detective work to find out which products you need to replace.

### What can we do?

Remember that manufacturers do not always have to declare toxins on their product labels. Buy or make alternative products. If you use alternatives, you reduce the risk to your family and the environment. Here a few toxic examples and suggested alternatives.

- **Non-iron fabrics.** These are treated with formaldehyde resin which becomes part of the fibre due to the way it is applied. Result: toxic fumes.

  *Alternative: use natural fibres wherever possible.*

- **Oven cleaners.** These contain sodium hydroxide.

  *Alternative: while oven is warm sprinkle the surfaces with water, followed by layers of baking soda. Wipe grease away. Rub resistant grease spots gently with very fine wire wool pads.*

- **Air fresheners.** They do not actually freshen air, they deaden your nasal passages or coat them with oil. They may contain chemicals such as xylene, ethanol, napthalene and so on.

  *Alternatives: use herbal mixtures or vinegar and lemon juice left in a bowl, scented candles and oils.*

- **Mothballs.** These are made from paradichlorobenzene, which is harmful to your liver and kidneys.

  *Alternative: use herbal products that act as repellents, cedar chips or cedar oil.*

- **Permanent-ink pens and markers.** These contain harmful solvents such as toluene, xylene, ethanol.

  *Alternatives: use water-based markers and pens.*

## Styrofoam

### Overview

What we call Styrofoam is actually polystyrene foam. This material is made from benzene (a known carcinogen), converted to styrene, and then injected with gases which turn it into a 'foam' product. The gases often used are CFCs, which eat ozone molecules, depleting the earth's vital ozone layer. The current alternatives to CFCs are not wonderful. One is HCFC which is 95 per cent less damaging than CFCs, but still a threat to the ozone layer. Others are pentane and butane – hydrocarbons that contribute to urban smog. So non-CFC foam merely replaces one kind of environmental problem with another.

## Facts and figures

- Polystyrene foam is completely non-biodegradable; it just will not go away. Even 500 years from now, that foam cup in which you had your coffee this morning might be sitting on the earth's surface.

- Because of its very structure – it contains large amounts of air – all Styrofoam. regardless of how it is made, takes up a great deal of space for its weight. This means that it wastes enormous amounts of precious space at already overloaded rubbish dumps.

- Polystyrene foam is deadly to marine life. It floats on sea surfaces, breaks up into pellets resembling food and is consumed. When turtles, for example, eat Styrofoam, its buoyancy keeps them from diving and clogs their systems so that they starve to death.

## What can we do?

There is no such thing as safe polystyrene foam. Do not use it. Refuse to buy egg cartons, delicatessen tubs and so forth made from foam products.

If you eat at fast food restaurants, ask for paper cups and plates.

*Make a note on how you could reduce the toxins in your home and workplace.*

**Notes**

_____

_____

_____

_____

_____

_____

# WAYS TO SUSTAIN RATHER THAN CONSUME

If you are a manufacturer, or a user of natural resources, you may want to consider the benefits in becoming a renewer as well as a user.

Many organizations, both large and small, are now adopting a policy of putting back as much as they take. For example, publishing companies are supporting forestry and tree-planting programmes, producers of plastic cartons and other items are supporting recycling schemes and other organizations are funding research into ways of dealing with pollution.

### *Reconsider. . .*

✦ **travel, distribution and commuting**

✦ **purchasing decisions and suppliers**

✦ **product design and packaging**

✦ **marketing activity**

✦ **energy conservation and management**

✦ **preventing pollution**

✦ **waste management**

Although it might be cynically claimed that these organizations are participating in such schemes for their own PR purposes, we must also understand that we all benefit from creating a renewable and sustainable economic system. If your business relies on trees, water or chemicals, then it is only economic sense to make sure that you are continuing the supply, and looking to ways to improve the technology that you use.

## Reconsider your current approach and standards

At the very highest level of environmental awareness, we begin to reconsider the values and the basis of our organization. This usually means taking environmental awareness more seriously, more of the time. It may also mean making significant changes in the way our organizations function. Pertinent questions to ask are as follows.

◆ Can products or services be made or bought locally, thereby avoiding expensive and damaging road transportation?

72

◆ Can you use the telephone instead of paper?

◆ Can you hold teleconferences rather than have delegates travel to a distant location for a meeting?

◆ Can some of your staff work from home? It is estimated that one in eight of all organizations already have some staff working from home, using computer and telephone technology – or teleworking as it is known. This form of working is expected to grow dramatically during the next ten to 15 years.

It holds many advantages for the organizations, which can save on office space, for the individual who can get more work done, and for the environment which experiences a reduction in road transport and therefore also in air pollution.

◆ Can you reconsider some of the products or production methods which you use? Over the last ten years many products have changed dramatically due to increasing consumer awareness of 'green' issues. For instance, ten years ago cars were sold on the basis of their speed and style; nowadays they increasingly are being marketed on their 'greenness', safety and economy. Most washing powder manufacturers now boast that their products contain fewer chemicals and clean using less powder.

Foods, toiletries and cosmetics are also now very different from what they were ten or 15 years ago. The success of the Body Shop, which uses only natural products and no animal testing, is one very visible example, but there are thousands of other product lines which have been similarly transformed, and this trend is set to grow over the next decade. Indeed politicians, who for years have paid no more than lip service to many environmental issues, are now increasingly beginning to recognize their attractiveness, not only from a vote-winning point of view but also from that of environmental common sense.

Take a moment to list some of the areas or ways in which your company or organization might reconsider some of the fundamental ways in which it operates or produces. For instance, introducing flexible working hours could greatly reduce traffic congestion, and therefore the level of pollution, which is far higher in stationary than moving traffic.

## The Valdez Charter

Following the disaster of *Exxon-Valdez* which ran aground and released billions of gallons of oil into the Alaskan environment, a group of powerful international investors formulated the Valdez Principles. These ten environmental principles which are set out below, must be accepted by a public

Environmental Awareness

company before the group allows its fund to be invested in the company's shares. It is the first significant recognition by the investment community of green credentials in organizations.

## The principles

1. **Protection of the biosphere**

   We will minimise and strive to eliminate the release of any pollutant that may cause environmental damage to the air, water, or earth or its inhabitants. We will safeguard habitats in rivers, lakes, wetlands, coastal zones and oceans and will minimise contributing to the greenhouse effect, depletion of the ozone layer, acid rain or smog.

2. **Sustainable use of natural resources**

   We will make sustainable use of renewable natural resources, such as water, soils and forests. We will conserve non-renewable natural resources through efficient use and careful planning. We will protect wildlife habitat, open spaces and wilderness, while preserving biodiversity.

3. **Reduction and disposal of waste**

   We will minimise the creation of waste, especially hazardous waste and, wherever possible, recycle materials. We will dispose of all wastes through safe and responsible methods.

4. **Wise use of energy**

   We will make every effort to use environmentally safe and sustainable energy sources to meet our needs. We will invest in improved energy efficiency and conservation in our operations. We will maximise the energy efficiency of products we produce or sell.

5. **Risk reduction**

   We will minimise the environmental, health and safety risks to our employees and the communities in which we operate by employing safe technologies and operating procedures, and by being constantly prepared for emergencies.

6. **Marketing safe products and services**

   We will seek products or services that minimise adverse environmental impacts and that are safe as consumers commonly use them. We will inform consumers of the environmental impacts of our products or services.

7. **Damage compensation**

   We will take responsibility for any harm we cause to the environment by making every effort to restore the environment fully and to compensate those persons who are adversely affected.

8. **Disclosure**

   We will disclose to our employees and to the public incidents relating to our operations that cause environmental harm or pose health or safety hazards. We will disclose potential environmental, health, or safety hazards posed by our operations, and we will not take any action against employees who report any condition that creates a danger to the environment or poses health and safety hazards.

74

9. **Environmental directors and managers**
   At least one member of the board of directors will be a person qualified to represent environmental interests. We will commit management resources to implement these principles, including the funding of an office vice-president for environmental affairs or an equivalent executive position, reporting directly to the CEO, to monitor and report upon our implementation efforts.

10. **Assessment and annual audit**
   We will conduct and make public an annual self-evaluation of our progress in implementing these principles and in complying with all applicable laws and regulations throughout our world-wide operations. We will work towards the timely creation of independent environmental audit procedures which we will complete annually and make available to the public.

*Consider ways in which your organization might sustain, rather than consume, natural resources.*

**Notes**

_____

_____

_____

_____

_____

_____

_____

_____

# CASE STUDY: AIR POLLUTION FROM CARS

Read the following case study, and decide how you would answer the questions which follow.

## Air pollution report

### Facts and figures

*Pollution from car and lorry exhausts has been increasing alarmingly in recent years. Although little research has been undertaken in the UK to show how this is affecting people's health, evidence from other countries suggests that there is cause for concern.*

*The main pollutants from traffic which affect human health are: carbon monoxide, ozone, nitrogen dioxide, and VOCs (volatile organic compounds).[1]*

### Health effects

*Various air pollutants are linked with diseases, such as asthma, hay fever, bronchitis and even cancer.*

*Children, especially the under-fives, are especially vulnerable, as are the elderly, people with existing respiratory disorders and pregnant women.[2]*

*The extent to which disease is exacerbated by air pollution, or perhaps in some cases caused by it, is unknown. The UK lags behind countries like the USA and Sweden whose Environmental Protection Agencies have estimated the numbers of their populations at risk from air pollution.[3]*

### Asthma

*There is clear evidence that pollutants – particularly ozone – may exacerbate asthma by acting as an irritant on the sufferer's sensitive airways. Pollution may also increase susceptibility to allergens which trigger attacks.*

*Deaths from asthma among young people have risen alarmingly in the past decade – between 30 and 60 per cent. During the same period, the volume of traffic on our roads – and the pollutants pumped into our air – rose by a similar percentage.*

### Hay fever

*One in five teenagers in Britain suffer from hay fever. General practice surveys show that the number of people attending their doctors for hay fever treatment has more than doubled in the last 10 years. Diesel exhaust in particular has been shown to increase people's susceptibility to pollen and other allergens.*

1. Department of the Environment (1991), *Digest of Environmental Protection and Water Statistics*.
2. *Air Pollution and Child Health*, London: Greenpeace.
3. *Populations at Risk*, London: Greenpeace.

## Respiratory infection

*Nitrogen dioxide and ozone both injure the smallest air passages of the lung increasing susceptibility to respiratory infections. A Swiss study has shown that symptoms, including cough, sore throat, fever, running nose and earache, increased in children with increasing exposure to nitrogen dioxide.*

*Individuals who have experienced a lower respiratory tract illness in early childhood are more likely to suffer from chronic lung problems in adult life.*

## Cancer

*Benzene, which comes mostly from vehicle emissions and evaporative losses from petrol, is a known carcinogen. The World Health Organization allows no 'safe' limit for benzene. Children living in urban areas have much higher blood concentrations of benzene than children in rural areas.*

*Studies in other countries have explored the possibility of a relationship between air pollution and childhood leukaemia; however, this possible connection needs further evaluation.*

## Traffic in the UK

*Choked and congested though our roads already seem, traffic levels are expected to double in the next 20 years.[4]*

*Even with the introduction of catalytic converters, we can expect to see no improvement in our air quality. Any benefits will be swamped by the sheer numbers of cars.[5]*

*Despite recent changes to road-building priority, the government still spends billions of pounds per year on building new roads – an amount which is at least three times more than that spent on public transport or alternative transport solutions. In the face of such imbalance, it is illogical to suggest that car use is a question of individual choice.*

*Without an efficient and safe public transport system, and proper facilities for cyclists and pedestrians, people do not have a real choice.*

*At present, more than 60 per cent of all car journeys in the UK are under five miles in length.[6] For the majority of people, these journeys could be made by foot or by bicycle. However, until cars cease to be given precedence over the methods of traffic, they will continue to be made by car.*

4. Department of Transport (1989), *National Road Traffic Forecasts (Great Britain)*, London: HMSO.
5. *Populations at Risk*, London: Greenpeace.
6. Department of Transport (1988), *National Travel Survey 1985/86*, London: HMSO.

# CASE STUDY: QUESTIONS

1.     *What can be done, or should be done, to resolve this situation?*

2.     *What is your experience of pollution and congestion and what steps could be taken to alleviate them?*

**PLEASE COMPLETE
BEFORE CONTINUING**

# KEY IDEAS

*Mark the top five ideas that are appropriate for your department or organization.*

1.  Always recycle newspapers and waste paper using local facilities.

2.  Always recycle bottles, plastics and tins.

3.  Use two sides of paper when writing reports or memos.

4.  Use the reverse side of used paper for scrap and notepaper where possible.

5.  When selecting suppliers, check whether the content of their products is as environmentally sound as possible.

6.  Whenever practical use the telephone instead of sending a letter or a memo.

7.  Choose products that have the least packaging.

8.  Drive in a manner that uses less fuel.

9.  Use public transport whenever possible.

10. Walk or cycle for short journeys when possible.

11. Input environmental ideas into planning and meetings.

12. Reduce the mileage travelled on business.

13. Source products and supplies from local suppliers to avoid unnecessary distribution.

14. Treat and dispose of waste products properly.

15. Always repair items where possible in order to avoid unnecessary extra consumption.

16. Completely avoid the use of CFCs and products containing dangerous chemicals or damaging production processes.

17. Switch off machines, equipment and lights that are not needed.

18. Use rechargeable batteries instead of the disposal type.

19. Encourage others to think in a more environmentally friendly fashion.

20. Select low-energy consumption equipment where possible.

> **PLEASE COMPLETE**
> **BEFORE CONTINUING**

# Chapter 5
# Learning Review

This chapter tests your environmental awareness.

Before starting this chapter, please take a few moments to make a note of any ideas or actions in the learning diary and log in Chapter 1.

# TEST YOUR KNOWLEDGE (1)

1.  How many cars are scrapped in the UK each year?

    a) 250 000

    b) 500 000

    c) 1 000 000

2.  How many gallons of sewage are pumped into Britain's seas, most of it untreated or only partially filtered?

    a) 50 million gallons

    b) 100 million gallons

    c) 300 million gallons

3.  In the last three decades what percentage of the world's rhinos have been killed for their horns?

    a) 55%

    b) 65%

    c) 85%

4.  How much water does the average Briton use in a year?

    a) 5000 gallons

    b) 10 000 gallons

    c) 50 000 gallons

5.  How many tonnes of paper do we put into our dustbins every week?

    a) 100 tonnes

    b) 500 tonnes

    c) 1000 tonnes

# TEST YOUR KNOWLEDGE (2)

1.    What proportion of British household rubbish is made up of packaging?

a)  a tenth

b)  a fifth

c)  a third

2.    How many pounds of plastic does the USA produce every year for every person on earth?

a)  2 lbs

b)  5 lbs

c)  10 lbs

3.    What percentage of Britain's paper is thrown away without considering recycling?

a)  28%

b)  54%

c)  73%

4.    According to government officials, what percentage of Britain's household rubbish could be reclaimed?

a)  30%

b)  50%

c)  60%

5.    What percentage of drinkable tap water is actually drunk?

a)  15%

b)  11%

c)  less than 1%

> **PLEASE COMPLETE**
> **BEFORE CONTINUING**

# TEST YOUR KNOWLEDGE (3)

1.  How many miles does the population of Los Angeles drive every single day?

    a) 142 million

    b) 115 million

    c) 55 million

2.  How far is the average car journey in the United Kingdom?

    a) 24 miles

    b) 53 miles

    c) less than 6 miles

3.  How much fuel does the average car consume in its lifetime?

    a) 860 gallons

    b) 1680 gallons

    c) 2250 gallons

4.  How many times their own weight in rubbish will the average adult generate in a lifetime?

    a) 110

    b) 250

    c) 600

5.  How many toilet rolls are used every year in the UK?

    a) 10 million

    b) 1 billion

    c) 2 billion

6.  How many cigarette lighters are thrown away every year in the USA?

    a)  60 million

    b)  235 million

    c)  500 million

**PLEASE COMPLETE**
**BEFORE CONTINUING**

# PRACTICAL SOLUTIONS

## Reducing air pollution

What steps can you and your organization take to reduce your contribution to air pollution?

## Reducing waste, consumption and use

How can your organization or department reduce waste, consumption and use?

## Recycling

What practical steps can you, or your company or department, take in terms of recycling and re-using items?

## Producing, choosing and using environmentally friendly products

What steps can your organization take in producing, choosing and using more environmentally friendly products?

> **PLEASE COMPLETE**
> **BEFORE CONTINUING**

# Chapter 6
# Environmental
# Action Plan

---

This chapter provides a blueprint that can be used to gather data about the consumption of resources, to identify factors that are most important and to develop a series of actions for reducing consumption.

# 100 PER CENT IMPROVEMENT PLAN

*The pessimism of thought is conquered by the optimism of action.*

The simple concept of this plan is that if you can achieve a 10 per cent reduction in consumption, usage and waste (including recycling), across ten significant areas, then this would lead to a 100 per cent improvement in creating a more environmentally sound and efficient company. You may also like to calculate the effect that these savings would have on profits. Solutions might vary from reducing, recycling or replacing materials; some may be easy and can be implemented straightaway; others may be more long-term.

The information required may not be too readily available, but you should be able to find or calculate it by means of a little detective work and by pressing the right buttons on your accounts department computer.

If your organization is going to implement effective and progressive improvements in the way in which it produces and consumes, then three steps must be taken:

1.      Measure what is important.

2.      Consider different factors to be important.

3.      Relate environmental improvements to business improvements.

Although your intentions in working and growing more in sympathy with the natural world may be morally and ethically sound, the reality is that most organizations operate for commercial gain. It is becoming increasingly recognized that being 'green' can be good for business. It encourages lower costs, less consumption and, with the legislative and economic trends to make both consumers and industries pay the true cost of damaging the environment, this can only increase.

# USING LESS POWER

1.  What is the annual cost of power and heating?

    a) Your office/you personally:      _____

    b) Your department:      _____

    c) Your company:      _____

2.  List three actions which you could take to help reduce this figure by 10 per cent over the next year:

    1.  _____

    2.  _____

    3.  _____

3.  How might this improve profits and competitiveness?

4.  What other benefits might be expected?

5.  What are the possible obstacles to overcome and plan for?

# USING LESS LIGHTING

1.  What is the annual cost of lighting?

    a)  Your office/you personally:      _____

    b)  Your department:      _____

    c)  Your company:      _____

2.  How many light bulbs are there in your building?

3.  How many are long-life?

4.  Could the wattage be reduced?

5.  List three actions which you could take to help reduce this figure by 10 per cent over the next year:

    1.  _____

    2.  _____

    3.  _____

6.  How might this improve profits and competitiveness?

7.  What other benefits might be expected?

8.  What are the possible obstacles to overcome and plan for?

# USING LESS FUEL

1.    What is the annual cost of spending on petrol and diesel fuel?

    a)  Your office/you personally:          _____

    b)  Your department:          _____

    c)  Your company:          _____

2.    List three actions which you could take to help reduce this figure by 10 per cent over the next year:

    1.  _____

    2.  _____

    3.  _____

3.    How might this improve profits and competitiveness?

4.    What other benefits might be expected?

5.    What are the possible obstacles to overcome and plan for?

# USING LESS PAPER

1.   What is the annual cost of spending on all forms of paper and cardboard?

   a)  Your office/you personally:                  _____

   b)  Your department:                             _____

   c)  Your company:                                _____

2.   What percentage of this is based on recycled product?


3.   List three actions that you could take to help reduce this figure by 10 per cent over the next year:

   1.   _____

   2.   _____

   3.   _____

4.   How could you switch to using more from a recycled source?



5.   How could you **double** the amount that you recycled over the last year?



6.   How might this improve profits and competitiveness?



7.   What other benefits might be expected?



8.   What are the other possible obstacles to overcome and plan for?

94

# USING LESS CHEMICALS

1.  What is the annual spending on hazardous or toxic chemicals? Consider both their purchase, additional safety measures, extra insurance and storage requirements and cost of disposal:

    a)  Your office/you personally: _____

    b)  Your department: _____

    c)  Your company: _____

2.  List three actions which you could take to help reduce this figure by 10 per cent over the next year:

    1. _____

    2. _____

    3. _____

3.  How might this improve profits and competitiveness?

4.  What other benefits might be expected?

5.  What are the other possible obstacles to overcome and plan for?

# USING LESS PACKING

1.    What is the annual cost of using and disposing of packaging?

    a) Your office/you personally:          _____

    b) Your department:          _____

    c) Your company:          _____

2.    What percentage could be recycled? (Hint: probably all of it!)

3.    List three actions you could take to help reduce this figure by 10 per cent over the next year:

    1.  _____

    2.  _____

    3.  _____

4.    How could you switch to using more from a recycled source?

5.    How could you **double** the amount that you recycled over the last year?

6.    How might this improve profits and competitiveness?

7.    What other benefits might be expected?

8.    What are the possible obstacles to overcome and plan for?

# USING LESS PROCESSING

1.  What is the annual cost of power involved in treating or processing products that you produce?

    a) Your department: _____

    b) Your company: _____

2.  List three actions which you could take to help reduce this amount of processing by 10 per cent over the next year:

    1. _____

    2. _____

    3. _____

3.  How might this improve profits and competitiveness?

4.  What other benefits might be expected?

5.  What are the possible obstacles to overcome and plan for?

# USING LESS DISTRIBUTION

1.   How many miles are travelled using road transport?

     |  | Business | Commuting |
     |---|---|---|
     | a) Your office/you personally: | _____ | _____ |
     | b) Your department: | _____ | _____ |
     | c) Your company: | _____ | _____ |

2.   How much does this cost per mile?


3.   List three actions which you could take to help reduce these figures by
     10 per cent over the next year:

     1.   _____

     2.   _____

     3.   _____

4.   How might this improve profits and competitiveness?




5.   What other benefits might be expected?




6.   What are the possible obstacles to overcome and plan for?

98

# CREATING LESS WASTE AND POLLUTION

1.  How many tonnes of waste/pollution does your organization generate in a year?


2.  What is the annual cost of disposing of waste and pollution generated by:

    a) Your office/you personally: _____

    b) Your department: _____

    c) Your company: _____

3.  List three actions which you could take to help reduce the amount of waste and pollution by 10 per cent over the next year:

    1. _____

    2. _____

    3. _____

4.  How might this improve profits and competitiveness?




5.  What other benefits might be expected?




6.  What are the possible obstacles to overcome and plan for?

# GREEN ATTITUDES

1.  On a scale of 1 to 10 (1 = totally ignorant or apathetic, 10 = very proactive), rate the level of environmental awareness of the following:

    a) Your office/you personally: _____

    b) Your department: _____

    c) Your company: _____

    d) Your suppliers: _____

    e) Your managers: _____

    f) Your directors: _____

2.  List three actions you could take to help increase the level of environmental awareness in practical terms by 10 per cent (by point improvement) over the next year:

    1. _____

    2. _____

    3. _____

3.  How might this improve profits and competitiveness?

4.  What other benefits might be expected?

5.  What are the possible obstacles to overcome and plan for?

# Appendix
# Suggested
# Answers to the
# Knowledge Tests

**Test your knowledge (1): suggested answers**

1. 1 million
2. 300 million gallons
3. 85%
4. 10 000 gallons
5. 1000 tonnes

**Test your knowledge (2): suggested answers**

1. (c) a third
2. (c) 10 lbs
3. (c) 73%
4. (c) 60%
5. (c) less than 1%

**Test your knowledge (3): suggested answers**

1. (a) 142 million
2. (c) less than 6 miles
3. (c) 2250 gallons
4. (c) 600
5. (c) 2 billion
6. (c) 500 million

# HEALTH AND SAFETY WORKBOOKS

The 10 workbooks in the series are:

| | |
|---|---|
| *Fire Safety* | 0 566 08059 1 |
| *Safety for Managers* | 0 566 08060 5 |
| *Personal Protective Equipment* | 0 566 08061 3 |
| *Safe Manual Handling* | 0 566 08062 1 |
| *Environmental Awareness* | 0 566 08063 X |
| *Display Screen Equipment* | 0 566 08064 8 |
| *Hazardous Substances* | 0 566 08065 6 |
| *Risk Assessment* | 0 566 08066 4 |
| *Safety at Work* | 0 566 08067 2 |
| *Office Safety* | 0 566 08068 0 |

Complete sets of all 10 workbooks are available as are multiple copies of each single title. In each case, 10 titles or 10 copies (or multiples of the same) may be purchased for the price of eight.

## Print or photocopy masters

A complete set of print or photocopy masters for all 10 workbooks is available with a licence for reproducing the materials for use within your organization.

## Customized editions

Customized or badged editions of all 10 workbooks, tailored to the needs of your organization and the house-style of your learning resources, are also available.

For further details of complete sets, multiple copies, photocopy/print masters or customized editions please contact Richard Dowling in the Gower Customer Service Department on 01252 317700.